Embrace Those Senior Moments!

'Cause every hard-working mind deserves a break

Those "senior moments" aren't just for seniors—the misplaced keys, forgotten appointment, and inability to remember what we had for dinner last night simply mean that we're busy, active, and have a lot of other things to think about!

So give yourself a creative break. Take time out to color a picture, laugh at a cartoon, think about a saying, and maybe solve a puzzle or two. And once you get back to your regular routine, you might even remember exactly where you left those misplaced car keys!

Aging is a journey...
and I'm trying to avoid
the potholes.

Word Search

Look carefully to find these uplifting words in the word search.

One astronaut asks another astronaut if he has ever heard of the planet Saturn. He replies, "I'm not sure, but it has a familiar ring."

Blue sky
Fluffy clouds
Flocks of birds
Sunshine
Rainbows
Dragonflies
Tree canopies
Balloons
Butterflies
Kites
Waving flags
Sunshades
Bumblebees
Raindrops
Snowflakes
Geese
Majestic pines
Helicopters
Hot air balloon
Fresh air
Hummingbirds
Monorail
Sunsets
Misty fog
Eagles
Angels

H U J P J T R E E C A N O P I E S B D G N H
N S A W E H O T A I R B A L L O O N A G B B
H U U H M I S T Y F O G K O Q E K P E E A U
K U T N L S T S G A L F G N I V A W S I L T
M E M W S F L U F F Y C L O U D S C E S L T
Z A U M B H Y K P R V Y T V K X C J E R O E
D R J T I I I T V S E N T N M R Q U G E O R
U R V E F N L N E M W S S M O U Y K J T N F
E Y A W S N G K E Y O D H E S E K Q Y P S L
Y S M I G T A B S X R N N A V V S S D O B I
R H W C N L I B I I L S O E I S E E O C X E
J D N O F D K C B R E Q H R D R U I O I S S
A I F W B B R F P E D J A L A L L L N L E O
W N O C F N O O B I V S A L Y I B F U E D S
K N G H C S I E P P N S K M C X L N R H A T
S I L E K W L A Y S E E J V G Y Q O Y R H E
P S T C L B T V R L O E S Z K D S G X L S S
W P O E M S Q Y G G V H D Y N Q H A O Q N N
W L R U S N M A R R G A T H J M V R H B U U
F F B W N I E Z J D I X K M W F R D O X S S

Solutions are in the back.

Thank God for senior moments!

- They clear your mind so you can focus on what's really important (whatever that is).
- They encourage the kids to do things for you that you don't want to do anyway.
- They serve as a good excuse to not recognize people you don't care to talk to.
- They get you off the hook when you forget the name of someone you see every day.
- They give you something to blame when you make a mistake.
- They give the kids something to blame when you embarrass them in public.

And most of all…

- They remind you that you're a living, breathing, still-functioning human being! (Only with a little mileage on you!)

We're not forgetful—

We simply choose to ignore all the stupid things we used to know.

Overheard at the gym...

"Just practicing my dance moves."

"Don't you think if God meant for us to touch our toes
He would have put them closer to our fingers?"

"Is she asking
us to do
downward *dog*?
She's *got*
to be joking!"

"I'm just saying, Noah, that I'd sure feel more comfortable if you'd put those two termites in a container."

Find 9 differences between the two pictures. Solutions are in the back.

Dear God, today I haven't lost my temper, made rude remarks, repeated gossip, or gotten ticked off at anyone. I haven't taken out my frustrations on other people, refused to do kindness, or run out of patience. But I'm just about to get out of bed now, God, and from here on, I'm going to need a lot of help.
Amen

How to Draw Birds with Letters and Numbers

Draw a funky bird with O, M, I, C, V, 7, i, 6

Draw a "O" for the head.

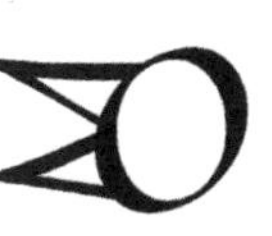

Add "M" for the open beak.

Draw a larger "O" for the body, "I" for each leg.

Draw a "C" and "V" for the wing. Add a dot for the eye.

Draw two "7's" and an "i" for the tail. Draw "6's" for details.

Smooth neck lines.

Draw an owl with 8, V, 7, E, M, W

Draw an "8" on its side for eyes.

Draw "V's" for beak and ear tufts, dots for the eyes.

Draw "7's" for wings.

Draw "E's" for claws.

Draw an "M" for the tail and "W's" for pattern on the chest. Add decorative details.

Draw an flamingo with S, O, V, C, U, 7

Draw an "S" for the neck.

Draw a large "O" and a "V" for body and tail.

Add a small "o" for the head. For the beak use two small "V's". Add a dot for the eye.

Draw a small "C" for the eye detail. Add a "V" inside the tail, a "U" for wing and top of legs. Draw long "7's" for the legs, small "V's" for the feet.

You know things aren't going well for yourself when you walk out of a memory-improvement class and can't remember where you parked your car.

Selfie

This puzzle is all about you! All answers follow "self"!

ACROSS

6 You might put yourself under it.
7 Too much of it goes before the fall.
11 Your thoughtful approval of you.
13 "Hey, here I am!"
14 Soundly adjusted.
15 You might nurse it.
18 Backward pat.
19 Egoist's expertise.
21 Be the king (or queen) of your castle?
24 You are all you need.
27 Approval!
28 Personal issue?
29 "Awww, poor me!"
30 Your potential.
31 You learned it all by yourself.

DOWN

1 You can't put a price on it.
2 It was at your own speed.
3 Figure yourself out!
4 You're this if you can think for yourself.
5 DIY.
8 Personal martial arts?
9 You don't need a doctor to do it.
10 "I will do this!"
12 Selfie.
16 "Can't I do anything right?"
17 You're the boss.
20 "I have a heart for me!"
22 Prophecy you make come true.
23 Aretha Franklin spelled it out for you.
25 DIYer's reading preference.
26 You walk away from it.

Solutions are in the back.

So True!

You're
only young
once –
but you can
be immature
forever!

Life's more fun
if you're cute...

You get away
with stuff.

Minutes at the
table don't put
on weight–

it's the seconds.

In a changing world,
one thing is
always certain:
You'll end up in the
check-out lane that
comes to a standstill.

Honey,
if you got it,
flaunt it.

Just be careful not to
throw your back out.

Drag your thoughts away from your troubles...
by the ears, by the heels, or any other way you can manage it.

Mark Twain

How to have a great day:

1. Open a document on your computer.

2. Title the document My Problems.

3. List your problems, and then close the document.

4. Now send the document My Problems to the Recycle Bin.

5. When the computer asks you, "Are you sure you want to delete My Problems permanently?" press Yes.

6. Feel happier?

If you ever find happiness by hunting for it,
you will find it, as the old woman did her lost spectacles,
safe on her own nose all the time.

Josh Billings

Connect the Dots

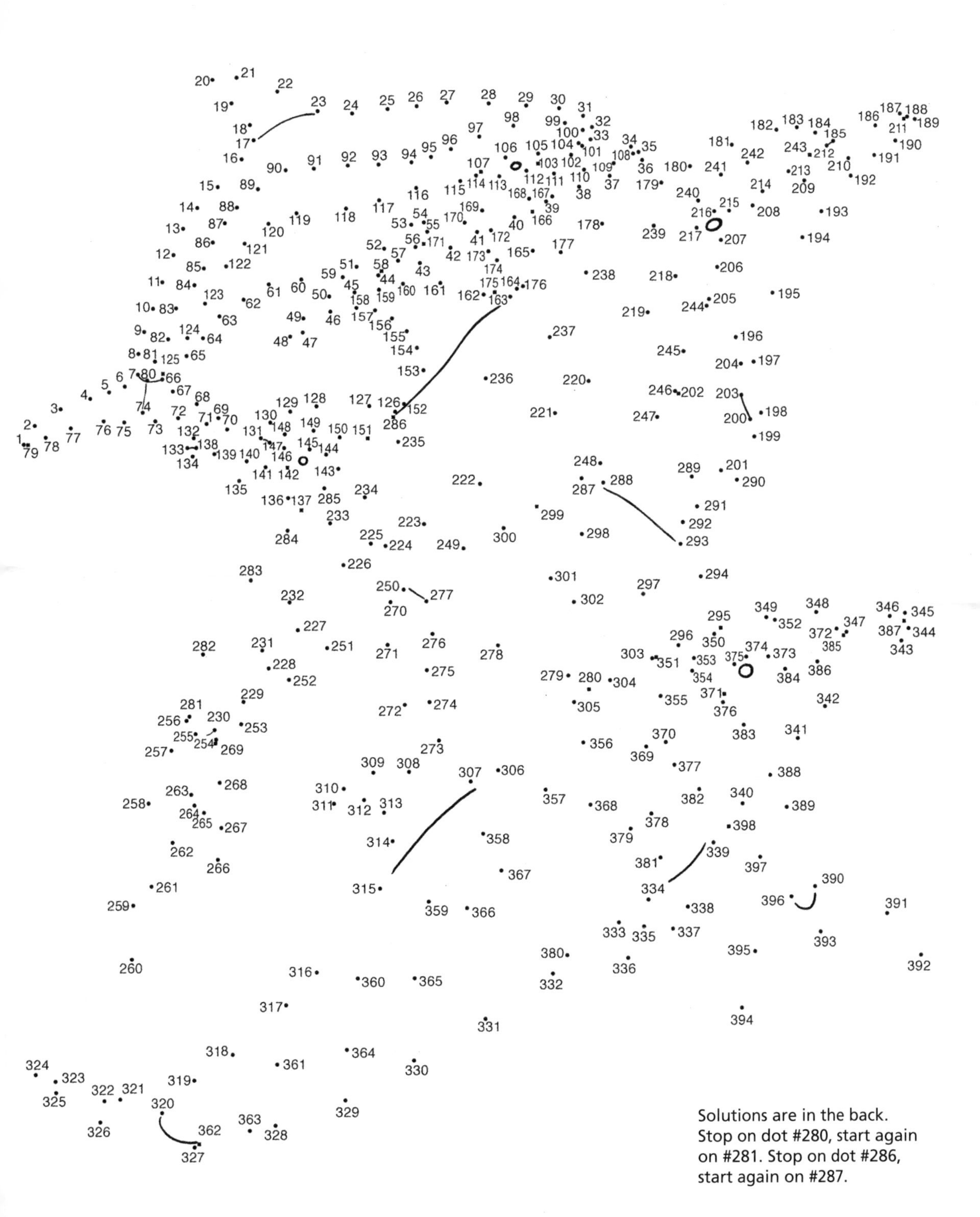

Solutions are in the back. Stop on dot #280, start again on #281. Stop on dot #286, start again on #287.

Word Search

Take a tour of the garden and find the flowers in the word search below.

Dandelion
Rhododendron
Dahlia
Peony
Honeysuckle
Zinnia
Orchid
Hibiscus
Daisy
Hydrangea
Azalea
Butterfly weed
Snapdragon
Coreopsis
Sunflower
Tiger lily
Geranium
Stargazer
Alyssum
Columbine
Wild Rose
Coneflower
Lilac
Begonia

```
S S F D A I S Y Z L P Z N P F S G O I V X Y
T G X F S U N F L O W E R E N I B M U L O C
A T B H F Q V H E M T S T I G E R L I L Y Y
R N R U I K O Z L P O X P R R W B M M F R H
G Z H G T B I V Z E E W P G R A I N O G E B
A J O X S T I K U O T B R E W O L F E N O C
Z E D F Q B E S S N P A E G N A R D Y H E Y
E E O S S I S R C Y B M U I N A R E G B P D
R B D Q Q N T M F U M S I G D Y H F F O O X
K B E P L I A K E L S T N V Y F Y P H P R L
C H N M Q Q M P C L Y B I L Z R U Y X I C I
M O D B U X T S D U K W U N O C A D G S H H
J B R D V S I P O R E C E T O S A I Z W I N
Q N O E K L S U O I A S U E S I A L L B D G
O H N A O I O Y B Z A G O S D T L X I H R I
N W T W I P U Y L L E B O R Y J B E K L A H
G H W D U N S V G A L Y L N D E D R D K A D
C M J V M V N I N W A X V I H L N H U N I Y
R K L Z N O C I S O Z H U D B O I O F E A A
A N Z W N V H C Z O A Z F X U A V W H U U D
```

Solutions are in the back.

Time with friends is the best time of all.

There's Nothing Like an Old Friend

A group of long-time friends met at a different restaurant on the first Tuesday of every month for food and conversation. They were all talking about how wonderful the cannoli was at the restaurant where they'd met the previous month. All, except Lisa who had been out of town that week. "So, where'd you go?" Lisa asked. Barb, the woman to her right, asked, "What's the name of the flower you give to someone you love? You know… The one that's red and has thorns." "Rose?" Lisa replied. "Yea, that's the one," Barb said. She turned to the woman on her right and said, "Hey, Rose, what's the name of the restaurant we went to last month?"

Friends are like...

tea bags. You don't know how strong they are until they land in hot water.

Friends are like…
fudge. Sweet, but nutty, too.

Friends are like…
pretzels. Completely twisted at times.

The language of friendship is not words but meanings.

Henry David Thoreau

It is one of the blessings of old friends that you can afford to be stupid with them.

Ralph Waldo Emerson

10 Things Good Friends Say

1 "Of course it's his fault – that goes without saying."

2 "I think some chocolate ice cream would solve the problem."

3 "Yes, I believe you know what your cat is thinking."

4 "No, you didn't over-react at all. He deserved it."

5 "...it's not your body that's a problem – they just don't make clothes that fit anymore."

6 "Definitely we're ordering dessert."

7 "Of course you should buy those shoes."

8 " 'Which one?' What are you talking about? Buy both!"

9 That's not a wrinkle – it's just a laugh line that shows you have a great sense of humor.

10 Do you need a shoulder to cry on? I'm on my way over right now.

optimism:
A cheerful frame of mind that enables a tea kettle to sing though in hot water up to its nose.

Positive Thinking

"I know I can, I know I can, I know I can...solve this puzzle!"

ACROSS

4 Mighty thought's might.
6 Positive conviction.
7 Purely positive thoughts.
10 It's a pleasure!
11 Positive thinking makes it.
13 You think funny with it.
15 Your thoughts __ your outlook.
18 You positively __ for the best.
19 You know it!
21 Stadium sound.
24 A positive frame of __ is a good thought!
25 Positive reflection. (hyph.)
28 Moody thoughts?
29 It's what to look on. (2 words)
31 How you think about it is how you see it.
32 Can do, if you think you can.

DOWN

1 Positive thoughts are good for it.
2 "In God we __."
3 Thankfulness.
5 It comes with certain thoughts.
8 You get what you __.
9 Dear thought?
12 Deciding thought.
14 Glass-half-full thinker has it.
16 Think "yes" to you!
17 Positive thoughts invite it.
20 Your thoughts determine how you take it.
22 Many can find one, even in adversity.
23 Thoughtful giver's attribute.
26 Positive greeting.
27 Cozy thoughts bring it to you.
30 Lovely thoughts' source.

Solutions are in the back.

"The good news is that you have a lot of liquid assets.
The bad news is that they've all gone down the drain."

Find 5 differences between the two pictures. Solutions are in the back.

Look on the bright side of life...
even if you have to squint a little.

Finish each day and be done with it.

You have done what you could; some blunders and absurdities have crept in; forget them as soon as you can. Tomorrow is a new day; you shall begin it serenely and with too high a spirit to be encumbered with your old nonsense.

Ralph Waldo Emerson

"I told her getting a tan was a bad idea, but nooooo...."

I have not failed. I've just found 10,000 ways that won't work.

Thomas A. Edison

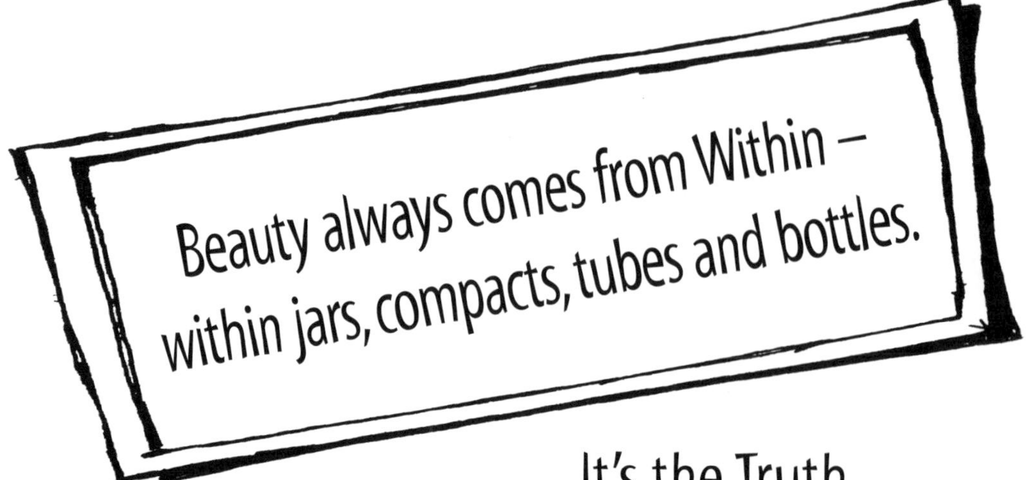

Here's Looking at You

A man moved into a retirement center, and he soon became aware of one woman who was always staring at him. Finally curiosity got the best of him, and he went over to the woman and asked her why she looked at him so intently. She answered, "Because you look like my third husband."
"Oh, I see," said the man. "How many times have you been married?"
"Twice," she replied.

It's the Truth

You know the mantra, "beauty comes from within"? We say it to youngsters and now it's time to say it to ourselves, and as many times as necessary. Physical beauty may fade, but inner beauty is something we can start cultivating, and deepen, at any age. If it takes you sitting yourself down for a heart-to-heart talk about what really counts in life...in a person...in a heart... then go ahead and do it. And then believe it, because you're telling yourself the honest truth!

There's an easy way to avoid wrinkles: unscrew the light bulb next to the bathroom mirror.

Connect the Dots

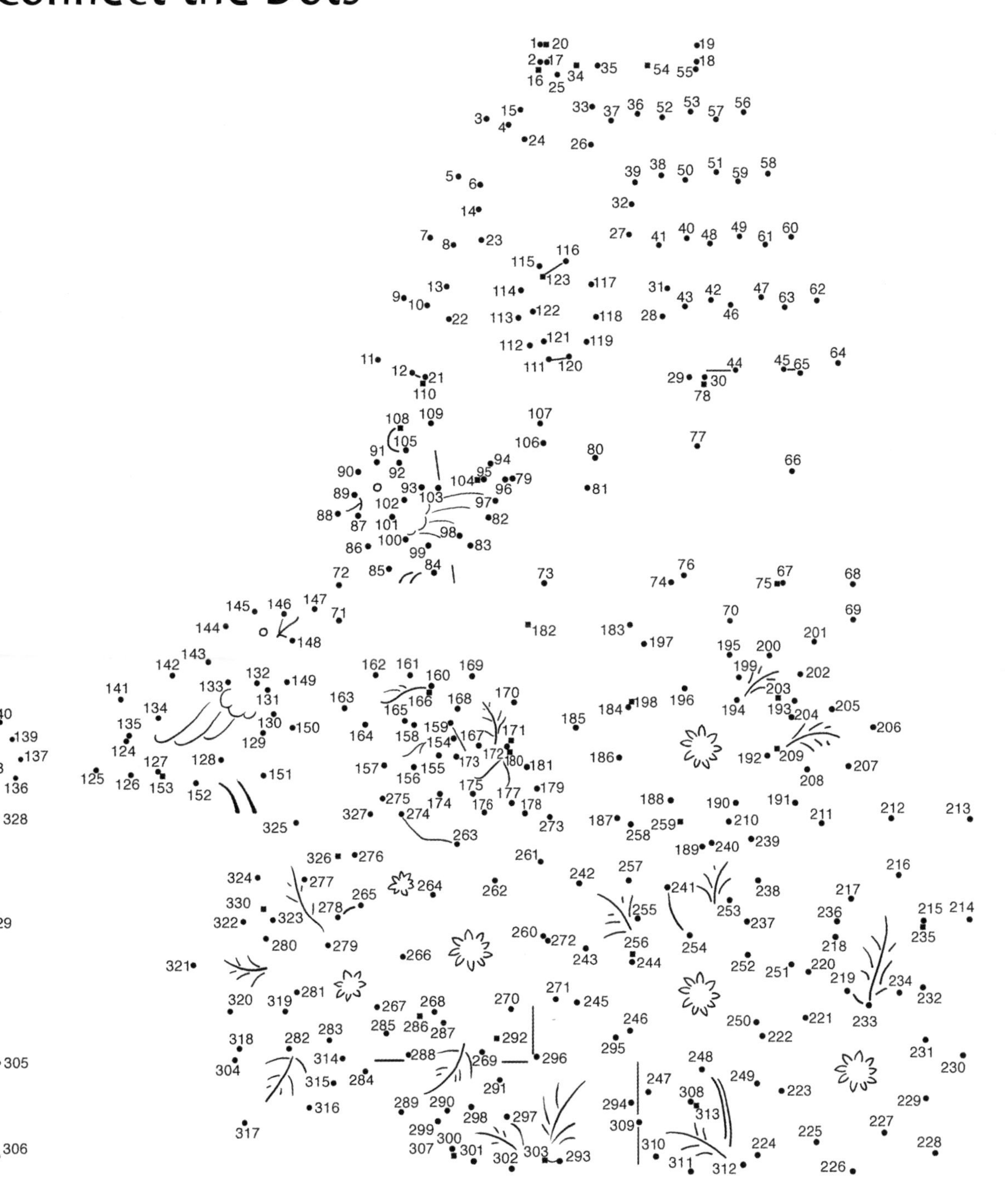

Solutions are in the back.

How To Draw A Still Life

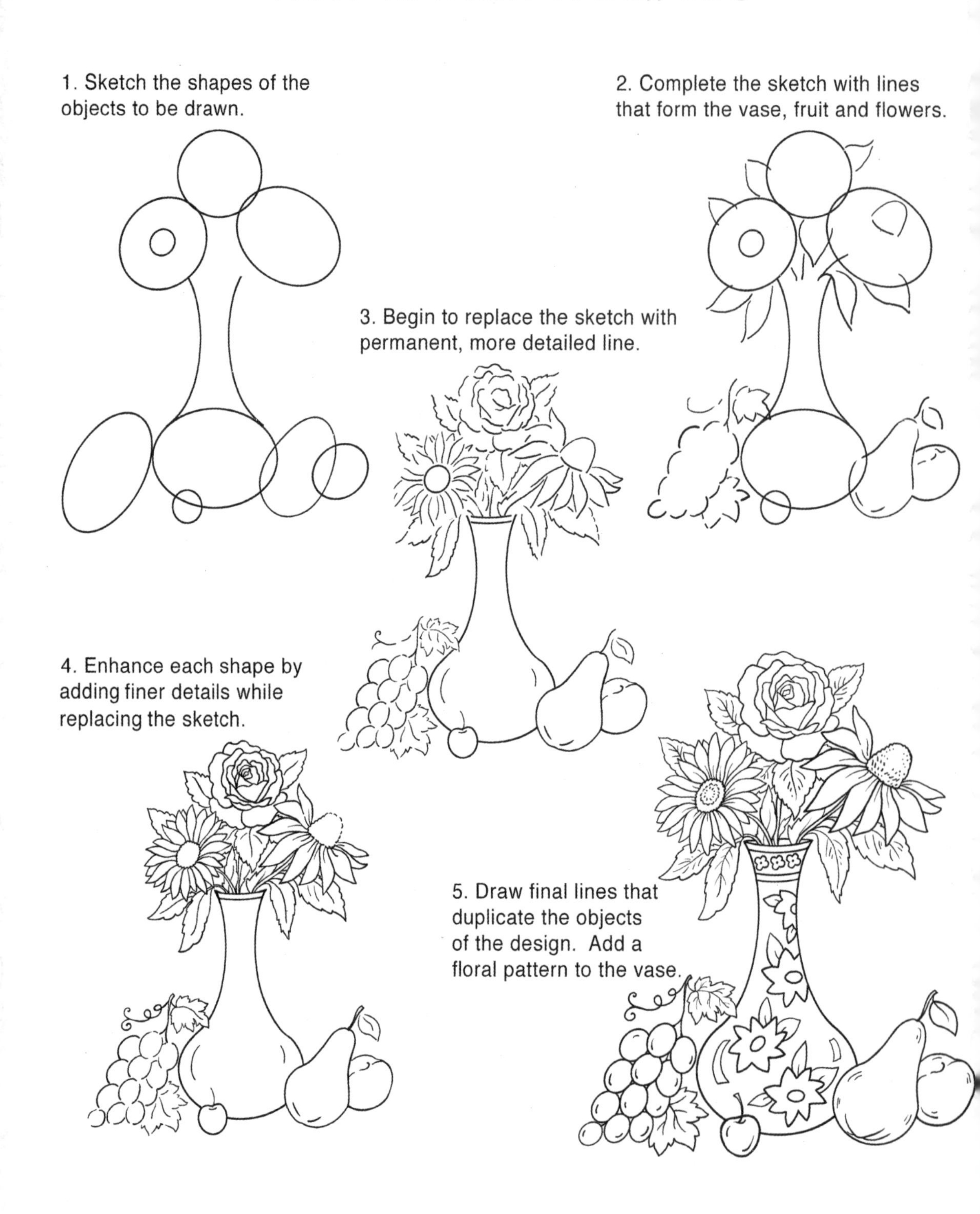

Mixed-Up Maxims

- Spend each day as if it were your last...and you'll be broke by sunset.
- A journey of a thousand miles begins...four words: I know a shortcut.
- It doesn't matter whether you win or lose... until you lose.
- You can't take it with you...or hearses would have luggage compartments.
- There's no fool like an old fool...although teenagers can offer some pretty stiff competition.
- Things improve with age...except at class reunions.

"These years are filled with wonder—wonder where I left my glasses... my keys...my truck..."

So *that's* where I put that!

It isn't our position, but our disposition, that makes us happy.

PERSPECTIVE

Whether we're in the workplace or out of it... spend our days earning an income or volunteering our time...digging in the garden or watching the sales figures...managing a home, business, or just ourselves (perhaps the most challenging task of all!), frustrations happen. We mingle with annoying neighbors, crabby coworkers, quirky teenagers, needy friends, and limelight-loving committee members.

Are they going to change? Nope. They'll continue to drive us nuts until *we* change—until we can look at them and realize we've got all the makings of a great comedy script every day, wherever we are, from dawn to dusk!

Don't let your age get you down,
it's too hard to get back up again.

A woman, concerned about her widening waist line, consulted a dietitian who told her that the best way to cope with her changing metabolism was to eat regularly for two days and then skip a day. "In two weeks, you'll lose five pounds," the dietitian promised. In two weeks, the woman reported back with the happy news that she had lost not five, but 15 pounds. "But I nearly passed out on the third day," the woman added. "From hunger?" the dietitian asked, "No," the woman replied. "From skipping."

They say that age is all in your mind.
The trick is keeping it from creeping
down into your body.

"But we've got to have raisins, Grandma!
How else are they going to be able to see?"

Find 6 differences between the two pictures. Solutions are in the back.

Follow the color key on the back cover for this color-by-number design, or create your own original color scheme

The older you get, it's funny how…

...what you thought you heard is so much more entertaining than what was actually said.

...you come to realize that some mistakes are way too much fun to make only once in life.

...your knees buckle, but your belt won't.

...an answer to "How do you feel?" can take up the better part of an afternoon.

...your back goes out more than you do.

...everything is over by the time you find your glasses.

Overheard at Grandma's house...

"Whatever you do, don't step on that square thing. Every time Grandma does, she lets out this awful loud scream!"

How To Draw A Cougar

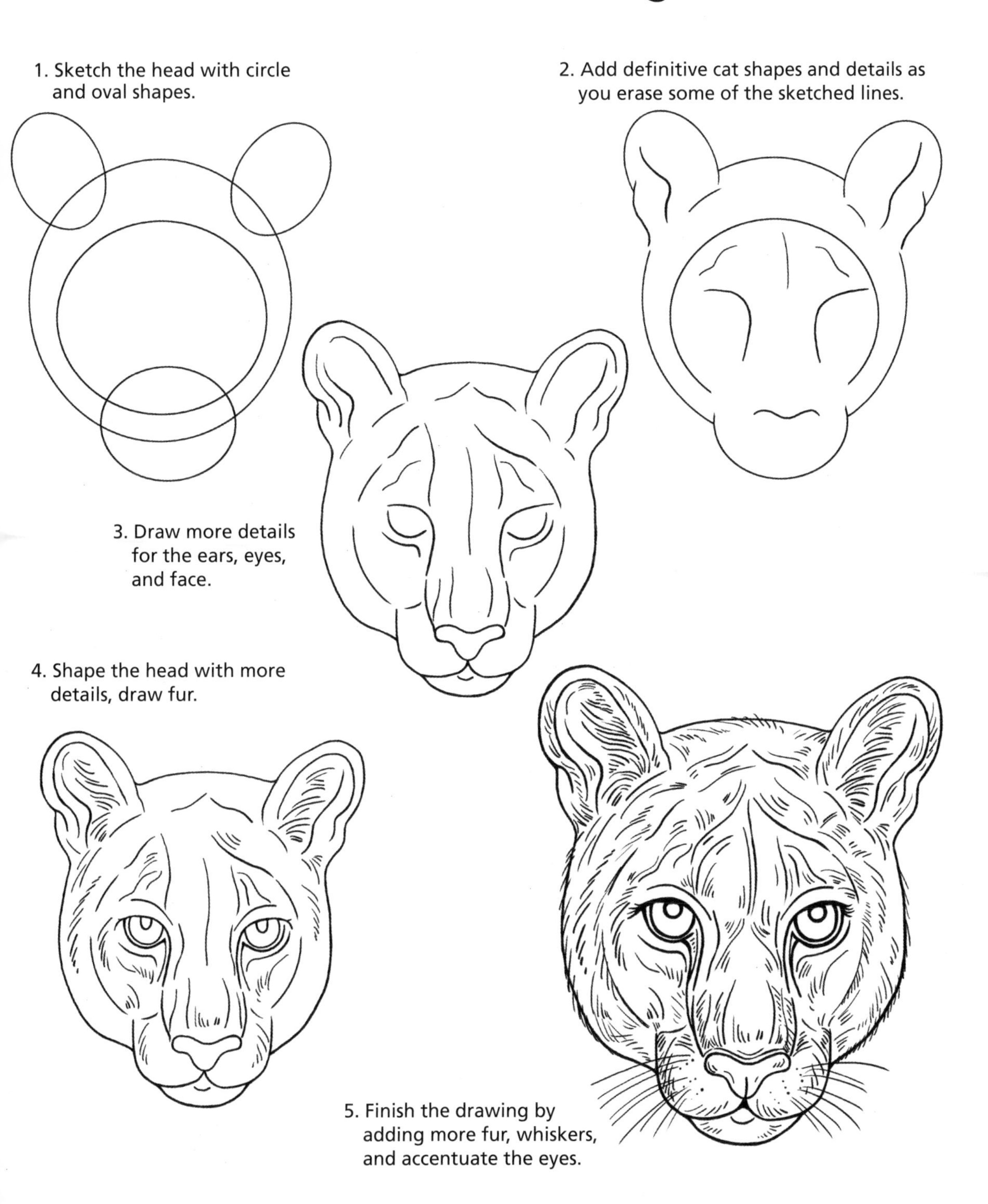

Winter is the time of year when people start going to places where they can pay two-hundred dollars a day to experience the same heat that they were complaining about all summer long!

Brrrr!

Warm up with this puzzle all about winter!

ACROSS

2 Controlled burn.
4 A romantic place for you and your flame.
9 Where you'll find the latest scoop?
12 Car part.
15 Cold cuts? (2 words)
16 Bright spots.
19 Not a baaad wrap!
21 Icy fella?
23 It might be patchy.
24 You could be below it.
25 Marshmallow go-with. (2 words)
27 Biting weather descriptor.
28 Sloping pastime.
30 Deciduous tree descriptor.
31 They're handy in the winter.
32 It's not clear to anyone.

DOWN

1 You might make this sport a goal.
3 Stand-offish stare?
5 Winter hangers.
6 Fall-back time for cool-down days.
7 They wander in the wind.
8 Fuzzy white kitty's moniker.
10 Personal portable rain roof.
11 Winter angler. (2 words)
13 They're not the cat's pajamas.
14 You might yearn to see one.
17 It could sleigh you!
18 Windbag's weather report!
20 That's thaw, folks!
22 It's a blast in some places!
26 Season's seasoning.
29 You can see it in the cold.

Solutions are in the back.

Caption This!

Dear God,
Whatever years may bring,
There's one thing that I pray –
Grant me a joyful attitude
And laughter every day.

Might as Well Laugh

Ever sat down in a restaurant next to a table full of seniors? Ever gotten together with a few longtime friends? More often than not, everyone was cracking jokes, telling stories, and laughing – heads-back, hands-on-the-belly laughing. At a certain age, we finally hit the point where we realize that really fantastic times can cost no more than a price of a cup of coffee. Times like this simply need our stubborn refusal to let anything come between us and another great day.

You know you're getting old
when it's not the food itself you talk about,
but whether you're supposed to take your pills with it.

The spirit of delight
comes in small ways.
Robert Louis Stevenson

I've never seen a smiling Face that was not Beautiful.

The soft glowing face on the cover of almost any glossy magazine tells you more than you want to know. Sure, it's another boost to our youth culture, but before you sigh because that skin's not yours anymore, consider this – That flawless complexion hasn't cried as much as you, but hasn't laughed as much, either. Those crow's-feet-free eyes don't reflect a lifetime of seeing and thinking and dreaming. That unlined mouth hasn't had the chance yet to comfort, encourage, guide, support. And say "I love you" ... knowing what it really means to love.

A little girl watched as her mother applied cold cream all over her face. "Why are you doing that?" the girl inquired.

"To make myself beautiful," Mom replied. Then she put the cap back on the jar of cold cream, pulled out a tissue, and began to wipe the cream off her face.

"What's the matter, Mommy?" the girl asked, "Are you giving up already?"

Word Search

"Look at that speed!" said one bird to another as a jet fighter zoomed over their heads. "Hmph!" snorted the other, "You would fly that fast too if your tail were on fire!"

Up, down, forward, backward, diagonally... find these birds...

- Flamingo
- Scarlet tanager
- Goldfinch
- Robin
- Cardinal
- Macaw
- Toucan
- Oriole
- Blue jay
- Bluebird
- Red finch
- Parrot
- Parakeet
- Grosbeak
- Mallard
- Pheasant
- Peacock
- Great blue heron
- Hummingbird
- Wood duck
- Cedar waxwing
- Kingfisher
- Woodpecker
- Indigo bunting
- Canary

```
S S G D J K V R G H U M M I N G B I R D M I
W Z C G M E B R P T R Y W A C A M G R J F P
X T I A L H O D R A L L A M M T W D E Q L A
F B G O R S K S V Y R Q D P Y X H M K V A R
Y F I O B L Q U S E Z I E I O I S L C X M R
S R F E L N E N R Z H A H N H U L Q E Y I O
O W A X N D O T K B C L R Q N I N D P R N T
F K B F S S F K T O Y E E Y B O E G D F G F
N G I W Z U H I C A N Z R L R X N C O T O P
P N H Z O W Z K N O N A G E I I U C O N L C
I I F Q X O E K T C N A H U T T L R W A R W
Z W K Y E B D N T A H E G N T D R T W S E F
R X R J E L K D C L U L U E R Z N T H A H E
K A T G J Z A T U L A B F I R L E Y C E S G
J W I F V C O N B C O G B U M E A G N H I V
T R R L J U I T I G K E O N K J X E I P F N
J A V H C V A L I D U J R A E V Q J F F G I
W D J A T E Z D T L R F R U B C P Q D U N B
V E N F R B N E B H M A L T U B F P E Z I O
W C A G I I F T Q T P B C X O T E O R G K R
```

Solutions are in the back.

EVERYBODY NEEDS A BUCKET LIST.

What are some of the items on your "bucket list"? Maybe you'll find a few of them included in this puzzle as you answer the quirky clues.

ACROSS

1 You fly one–with you on it!
3 Some do it with dolphins.
7 Pile in the car!
10 Take the plunge. (2 words)
12 It will make you run.
13 Whitewater way-to-go.
18 Hang on at the end of your rope. (2 words)
19 It takes a leap of faith.
20 You'll float up there! (2 words)
23 Is there a mountain high enough?
24 Put on your walking shoes!
25 Say "yes," and meet a need.

DOWN

2 It's on the rocks.
4 You can book it.
5 It's full of hot air.
6 Be at sea.
8 It will put you among reefs. (2 words)
9 You might get waved at.
11 Learn to play.
14 You'll be well-schooled.
15 You'll go places.
16 Two-wheeled thrill.
17 It's a jungle out there!
21 You'll use scales with this one.
22 It takes all colors.

Solutions are in the back.

Adventures in "Adapting"

What Goes Around...

Two 50-year old women had lived on a farm all their lives, and they decided it was high time they go into the city and see the sights. Awed at one of the towering office buildings, they walked in to the lobby and found themselves facing a set of metal doors. Just then the doors opened and an old lady walked in. A few minutes later, the doors opened again, and a young woman walked out. The farm women looked at each other, dumbstruck. "Next time those doors open," said one, "I'm gettin' in that thing!"

Remember when...

- Milk, eggs and sunshine were considered good for you?
- You chose your cereal for the toy, not for the fiber content?
- Your car's high beam light switch was next to the clutch?
- The only keyboard you owned was on the piano?
- More people counted their blessings instead of calories?
- The only web you knew about was the one hanging from your basement ceiling?

"Organic food? No thanks! I need all the preservatives I can get!"

Explore. Dream. Discover.

Twenty years from now you will be more disappointed by the things you didn't do than by the ones you did do. So throw off the bowlines. Sail away from the safe harbor. Catch the trade winds in your sails. Explore. Dream. Discover.
Mark Twain

The real voyage of discovery consists not in seeking new landscapes, but in having new eyes.
Marcel Proust

The person who has lived the most is not the one with the most years but the one with the richest experiences.
Jean-Jacques Rousseau

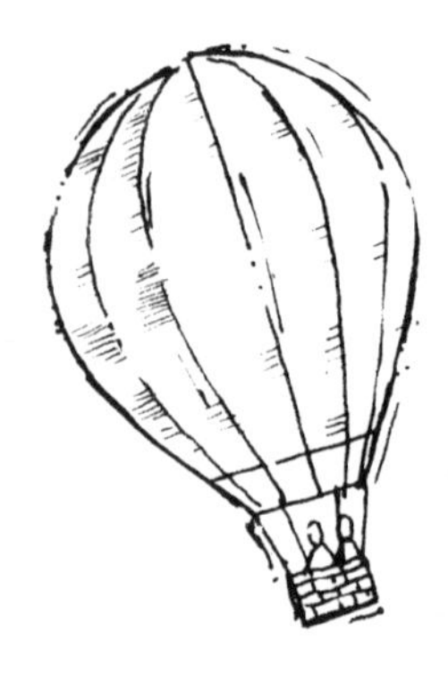

Though we travel the world over to find the beautiful, we must carry it with us, or we find it not.
Ralph Waldo Emerson

Not until we are lost do we begin to understand ourselves.
Henry David Thoreau

They travel lightest who carry the least amount of baggage.

Life is a journey—
it's not the destination that counts so much as who you have along for the ride.

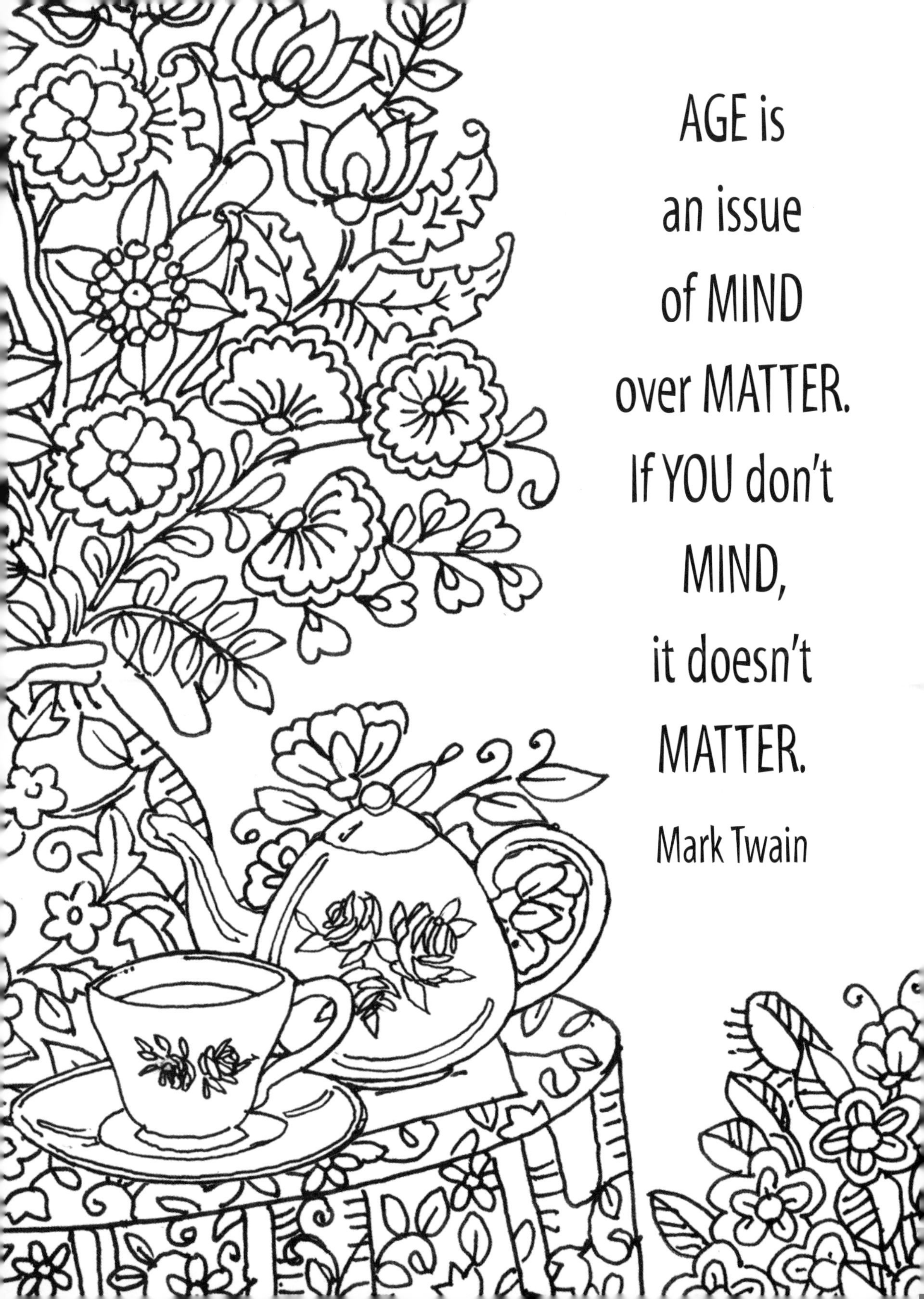
AGE is
an issue
of MIND
over MATTER.
If YOU don't
MIND,
it doesn't
MATTER.
Mark Twain

What's Up?

Suppose you tell Age what's up. It's standing there tapping its feet and awaiting instructions, so you'd better start barking some orders now. You sure don't want Age telling you what to do!

Start now. Here are a few ideas for starters. Say:

"Age, throw away all those negative feelings and stereotypes littering my head. And I don't mean recycle them – get rid of them!"

"And then you know what? Get out of my way—I've got things I wanna do!"

Whatever you are, be a good one.

Abraham Lincoln

What If?

- You never tell yourself you're too old to start... or to give it a try?
- You refuse to accept stereotypes... not about others, and not about yourself?
- You think, speak, and act on the outside as young as you feel on the inside?
- You smile, laugh, and enjoy life for no other reason than because you can?
- You take advantage of being the age you are... because you can?
- You make dreams come true for yourself... and even for others? Because you can.

And if not now, when?

The art of being wise is the art of
knowing what to overlook.
William James

A man should never be ashamed to own that he has
been in the wrong, which is but saying...
that he is wiser today than yesterday.

Jonathan Swift

Words of wisdom for the wise…

- Despite all the new and improved headache relievers, there are still headaches.
- Always go the extra mile, especially if what you're after is a mile away.
- Brain cells come and brain cells go, but fat cells stay with you forever.
- The colder the X-ray machine, the more of your body you will be asked to put on it.
- Be true to your teeth, or they will be false to you.
- Never lie to CAT Scan technicians, because they can see right through you.
- Don't be old until you have lived.

Some search for happiness at the end of a rainbow;
the wise find happiness even while standing in the rain.

How To Draw An Angel

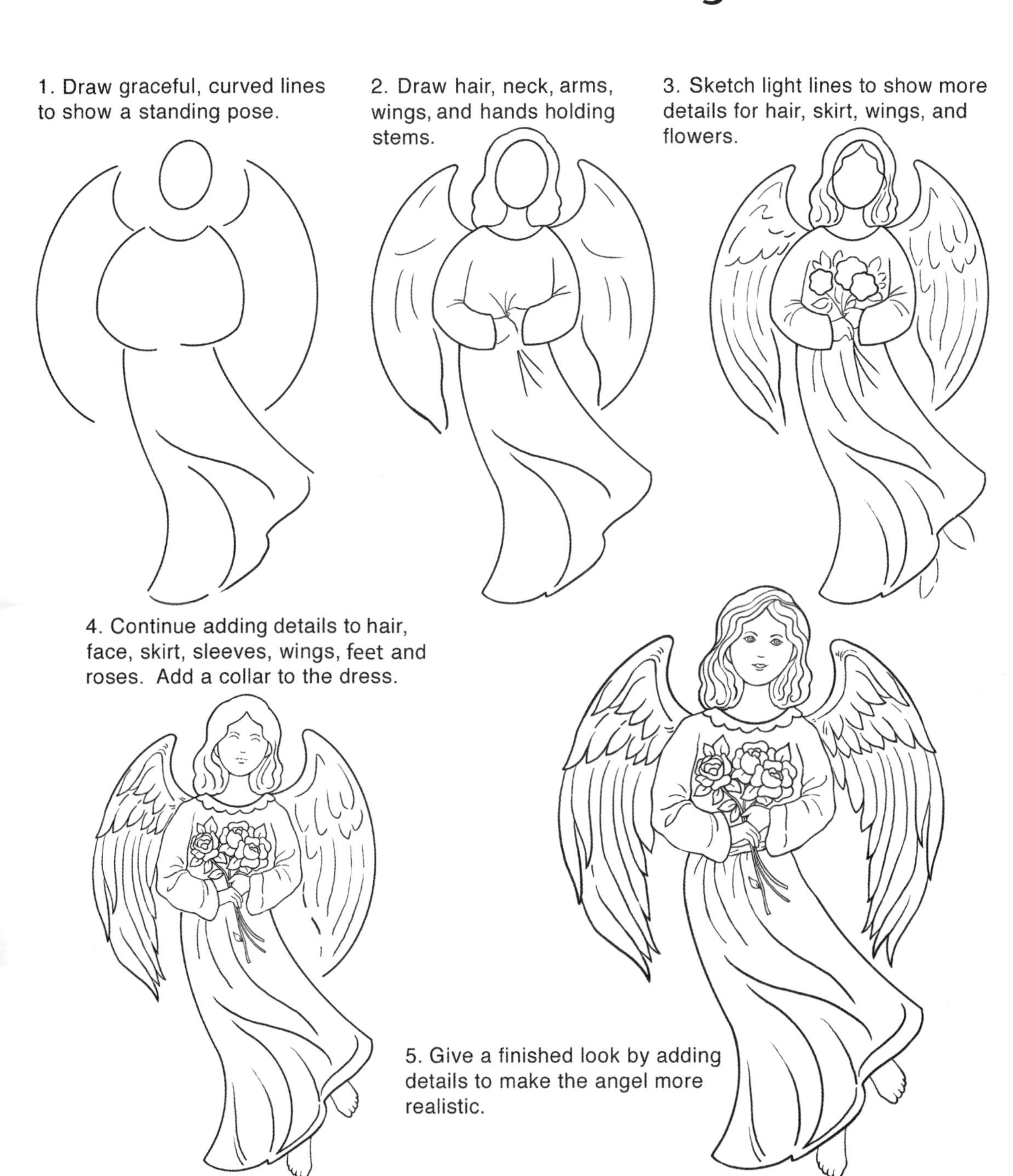

Most folks are as happy as they make up their minds to be.
Abraham Lincoln

Feelin' Fine!

Every answer follows "Happiness is…"

ACROSS

2 Present.
4 What you hope a gadget will do.
5 Happiness out loud.
7 You can believe it.
9 It's cheesy bliss, for some.
11 Heart's happiness.
12 Second serving?
15 X marks the spot.
16 Sweet ones.
17 You might have a role in it.
21 Dictionary's offer.
22 Roof-sharers.
23 They could be online.
24 Everything's better if you get a sense of it.
26 You can opt for one.
27 Day's ray.
30 Reason for livin'.
31 It's sure to satisfy.

DOWN

1 You're at liberty to have it.
2 It's in the telling.
3 There's only one!
6 Well-being.
8 Make it a good one!
10 Cool lick. (2 words)
13 Slice of happiness?
14 It lies between too little and too much.
18 Visual happiness. (2 words)
19 Happy occasion's ring.
20 You were born with it.
25 Spa's offer.
28 Happiness to your ears.
29 Uplifting conversation.

Solutions are in the back.

Old Friends Are The Best

You gotta
let your
greatness
shine!...
even if it
annoys others.

The great thing about old friends is we get to reminisce about the memories we've made, the laughter and tears, treasured times we've shared...and let's just stop right there. No need to go into all the stupid stuff we used to do.

"I NEVER REPEAT GOSSIP...
so listen close the first time."

May this day be overflowing with peace, happiness and love.

Sunshine and Music

A laugh is just like sunshine.
It freshens all the day,
It tips the peak of life with light,
And drives the clouds away.
The soul grows glad that hears it
And feels its courage strong.
A laugh is just like sunshine
For cheering folks along.

A laugh is just like music.
It lingers in the heart,
And where its melody is heard
The ills of life depart;
And happy thoughts come crowding
Its joyful notes to greet:
A laugh is just like music
For making living sweet.

Author Unknown

You are never too old to have a happy childhood.

The two most important days in your life
are the day you are born
and the day you find out why.
Mark Twain

The older you get, you discover that...

- Failure isn't permanent
- Worry isn't worth it
- There's humor in almost everything
- Each morning you wake up is a good morning
- Time is more precious than you ever thought
- You've survived some mighty hard times
- Gratitude is essential
- Other people's opinions don't define you
- Money isn't everything...really.

Teacher: "What's something important that didn't exist twenty years ago?"
Student: "ME!"

Find 5 differences between the two pictures. Solutions are in the back.

Q: What's the invention called that lets you see through the thickest of walls?
A: It's called a window.

What's New?

What do you think could have inspired these inventions?

ACROSS

1 Jelly go-with. (2 words)
3 It used to be for the birds.
4 Widest web.
6 It keeps things together.
10 It lets you know how far you've come.
11 Sound box.
13 It's a fair sight. (2 words)
16 You might be attracted to them.
17 Italian staple.
19 It has its ups and downs.
21 Frozen treat.
27 It used to be black and white.
28 Sky floaters.
29 Launchpad booster.
30 Hose.
31 What's the chance you'll get off the couch to change channels?

DOWN

1 It will help you put on a coat. (2 words)
2 It's about time!
5 You find them in closets.
7 You might woof these down! (2 words)
8 Fragrance.
9 Cheesy invention?
12 Carriages minus the horse.
14 You can have one even if you're not sitting down.
15 Finger bling. (2 words)
18 It used to be floppy.
20 Sometimes this, sometimes the hole.
22 Turf treader. (sometimes 2 words)
23 LP player. (hyph.)
24 You're write to guess this one! (2 words)
25 Hal, and others.
26 You can scale down this.

Solutions are in the back.

With Most Things In Life, It's Best to Keep It Simple

Special texting abbreviations (in preparation for the senior years):

BFF: Best Friend Fainted
BYOT: Bring Your OWN Teeth
FTW: Forgot The Word
FMM: Forgot My Meds
FWIW: Forgot Where I Was
CBM: Covered By Medicare
LMDO: Laughing My Dentures Out
TGIF: This Gal Is Forgetful
WAIT: Who Am I Texting?
BTW: Bring The Wheelchair
ROFLCGU: Rolling On Floor Laughing… Can't Get Up
GGLKI: Gotta Go, Laxative Kicking In!

"Honey, the phone is still ringing. You're answering the remote control."

There's no better blessing
than a good friend...
except a good friend who
grows to be an old friend.

What Friends Do

- Friends are those rare people who ask how you are and then wait to hear the answer.
- A true friend helps us think our best thoughts, do our noblest deeds, be our finest selves.
- Friends are the ones who go with you when the going gets tough.

Just Because

Because we get the giggles
and laugh until we cry,
And know if someone's hurting,
with just a simple sigh—
Because we get together
and share "remember whens,"
We share the joy of being
the very best of friends!

Special times, forever to hold...
Memories with friends are
worth more than gold.

True Blessings

May God grant you always
a sunbeam to warm you,
a moonbeam to charm you,
a sheltering angel
so nothing can harm you.
Laughter to cheer you,
faithful friends near you,
and whenever you pray,
heaven to hear you.

The brighter
your light
shines,
the easier
it is
for others
to find
their way.

The light
of the eyes
rejoiceth the heart.

Proverbs 15:30

Caption This!

"

"

"

"

"

"

"So if I give thanks for the broccoli, will God know I'm lying?"

Find 5 differences between the two pictures. Solutions are in the back.

Gratitude is the Heart's Memory.
Proverb

Going Forward

Gray, silver, salt-and-pepper—call it what you will. We know what you're talking about. There are also the little thin lines settling in to stay. The upper arms that aren't quite as firm as they used to be. Unlike your car, you don't come with a reverse gear. So all you can do is go forward with a smile – and gratitude. Gratitude for the many good times you've had, for the tough times you've come through, and the gift of today. Gratitude is a grand traveling companion wherever you are on the road of life.

Oh, no! Those senior moments,
Wrinkles and gray hair—
That jiggle in my middle
(Wish it were not there).

So Humor, Love, and Laughter,
You're my new best friends
And we'll face free and fearless
Everything life sends.

For it's not age that matters,
But a youthful heart
That says the best is coming—
Now is just the start!

If you want to feel rich,
just count all the things
you have that
money can't buy.

Judging by my
Laugh Lines,
you'd think my
life's been a Riot.

It's a Gift

It seems only yesterday you would hold up four fingers and make sure your grandma knew you weren't four, but four and a half! Then you spent a good part of your teens trying – praying! – to look older than your tender years, and now...well, now you don't want to think about age at all. But do think about it. Think about the blessing of being here this day...of having done, seen, and experienced so much...of the memories you wouldn't trade for anything...of being who you are, where you are.

If you want to know what heaven looks like, make someone smile.

Dogs Bein' Catty...

He who laughs last... probably doesn't get the joke.

Being this adorable is exhausting.

She's in great shape for someone her age.

Well, *Waaay* back when *she* was born, things were built to last.

Draw Animals with Letters and Numbers

Draw a Dog with O, U, C, W

Draw an "O" for the head.

"U's" become ears and muzzle. Add eyes and nose.

Use a "C" for the body, "W" for the legs, small "U's" for the paws.

Draw a "C" for the tail.

Smooth the lines and add details for the finish.

Draw a Cat with O, 3, 4, V, J

Draw two "O's" for the body.

Add "3's" for feet, a "4" for the nose, "V's" for the ears, dots for the eyes.

Remove and smooth some lines.

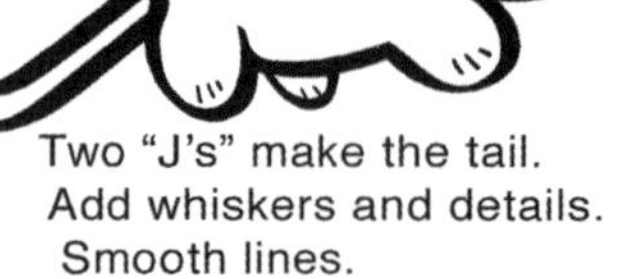

Two "J's" make the tail. Add whiskers and details. Smooth lines.

Draw a Rabbit with O, U, C, 6, Y

Draw two "O's" for the body, a "U" for the muzzle.

Draw "U's" for ears and a "C" for the lower body.

Draw a "C" for the tail, "U's" for the legs. Add a dot for the eye.

Complete details for the ears, "6's" for curls in the tail, a small "Y" for the nose. Smooth shapes.

Follow the color key on the back cover for this color-by-number design, or create your own original color scheme.

Middle Age is When you're Old enough to Know better, But still Young enough to Do it.

Bless the Day

Remember the gap between summertime and Christmas? Light years apart! But now it seems we're putting away the barbeque grill and getting out the mistletoe on the same weekend. Maybe this is God's way of saying, "Hey! Why don't you slow down? Because, like you've discovered, time passes fast. Always has, but now you know. So why do you keep putting all the good stuff off until 'someday'?" Today's the day to do something fun. Like untangle the twinkle lights? Nah. Something you actually want to do. Learn to knit. Bake a pie. Watch the sun set.

Write it on your heart that every day is the best day in the year.

Ralph Waldo Emerson

Connect the Dots

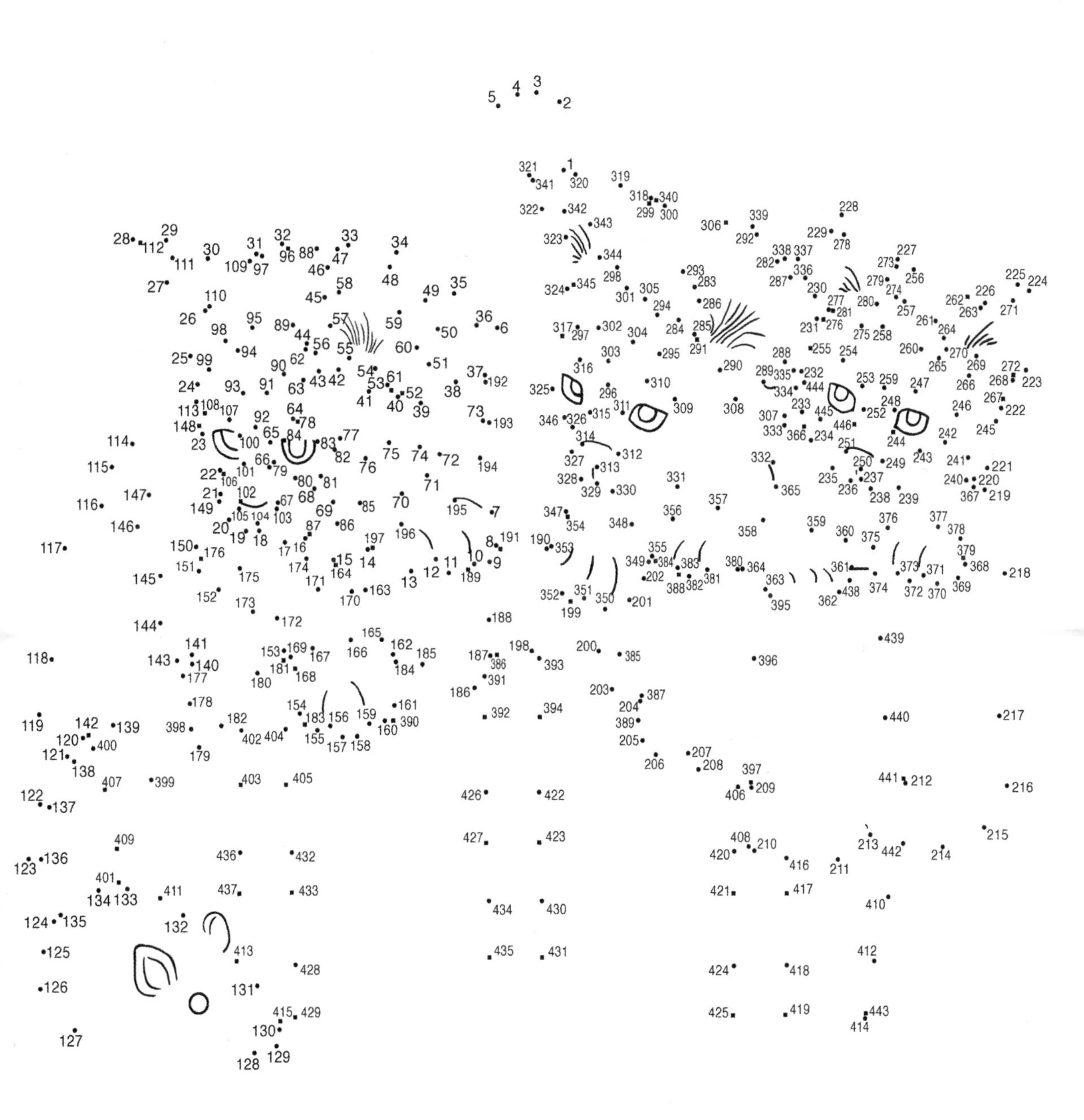

Solutions are in the back.

A good laugh is like manure to a farmer. It doesn't do any good until you spread it around.

Too Funny!

You might find yourself laughing at this puzzle!

ACROSS

2 Jollity.
3 Unkempt canine's tail? (2 words)
6 Non-rational joke?
8 They're jest like us!
9 Owl funny was it, anyway?
10 Field humor?
15 It's at your elbow. (2 words)
16 Animated humor.
18 They're contagious!
20 Tragedy's partner.
21 You get a sense of it.
23 Anecdotally, Queen Victoria wasn't.
25 There was once a witty rhyme...
26 Queue at the beverage table? (2 words)
27 Rap-a-Tap joke? (2 words)

DOWN

1 Fun for the birds?
2 Handy speakers?
3 Worn humor.
4 High school club.
5 Seasonal laughter. (3 words)
7 They're all for show.
11 Purler's tale?
12 Burst of humor.
13 Clipped quip. (hyph.)
14 Soundless laugh.
17 Laughable pratfall.
19 Groaners.
20 Laugh in low gear?
22 Picture strip.
24 Rising laughter?
26 Laughable language.

Solutions are in the back.

**Did you hear about the chicken that walked into a restaurant?
"We don't serve poultry," the manager said.
"That's okay," replied the chicken.
"All I want is a cup of coffee."**

Take a break from the daily grind to find these words.

Hot coffee
Iced Tea
Dark chocolate
Muffins
Cheesecake
Fresh fruit
Cocoa
Cappuccino
Strawberries
Truffles
Tiramisu
Sorbet
Steaming cider
Apple pie
Peach cobbler
Baklava
Gelato
Mocha latte
Malted milk
Cinnamon rolls
Espresso
Key lime pie
Spiced chai
Croissants

G X T C W F S Q Y V R W O N I C C U P P A C

G H J I W W L M Z Q E E F F O C T O H O K R

B A D N S H H U T E B R O S V A F U C H U S

I C D N V N G F E E T A L O C O H C K R A D

D L P A U Y D B N I A W C W I Z U Q R Q H P

P O G M Q K D D Z B P N J P F X O P Z M I W

S A T O T S V S E H K E V U E X J N O A W F

P V X N P E T S C J D Z M M S Y H I R L X M

I R S R G G S E U R S D F I O I Z B N T V O

C E V O D B P P A J O E O J L L M X U E Z C

E L T L V P S E R M C I I A P Y W A I D W H

D B I L D S R L K E I S S R E U E J R M B A

C B U S V D C N M A S N S S R I D K V I Z L

H O R V A M C K V Z C S G E A E P N L L T A

A C F H V A O Y E G S E O C L N B E R K L T

I H H F A G C I B V X G S S I F T W L R B T

E C S M L V O I F W X N I E Z D F S A P V E

U A E N K F A A E T D E C I E A E U S R P H

S E R H A F M A H G E L A T O H G R R C T A

E P F R B P M U F F I N S X O N C R G T A S

Solutions are in the back.

When things get unraveled, the threads of friendship hold us together.

Friends

are angels, sent to us on the wings of a blessing.

Sometimes I think that friends are like the angels of life who just happen to be human beings. They are the ones who watch over you with a kind of loving and nurturing style that supports the things you do and the hopes and dreams that give meaning to your life. Your angels are always merciful, seeing you with the best possible intentions, holding you in the best possible light.

EXERCISE:
a series of strenuous movements that converts fats, sugars, and starches into aches, pains and chocolate cravings.

How To Draw A Fawn

1. Use ovals and curved lines to indicate the curled up pose of a fawn, showing body, head and muzzle, ears and hind leg.

2. Begin streamlining shapes, erasing first drawing where necessary.

3. Continue organizing shapes making lines more graceful, indicating more fawn details.

4. Sketch light lines where the rows of spots will be. Add more details to the eyes and muzzle.

5. Begin sketching shapes for the spots erasing lines first sketched. Add more details for the tail, ears, face, legs and fur.

6. Finish the fawn drawing with more fur and details where needed.

EVERYTHING IS BETTER WHEN SHARED WITH A FRIEND.

Here's a hint to working this puzzle:
Just think of good times with a best pal.

ACROSS

1 They're fiery in Ephesians 6:16
6 Fib
9 Sodom sight
12 Boise locale
13 Bible olive product
14 Heat meas.
15 Ancient Indian
16 __ Dolorosa
17 Cut-up
18 Mature
20 Selfie
22 Friends' ways __ them to you
25 Interest-charger
26 Girlfriend's name, maybe
27 When you speak, friends do this
29 Cold-weather dish
31 You might do this with a friend
32 You need it when reproving a friend
36 When you call, friends do this
39 Feathery wrap
40 You might share one with a friend
43 Boston team (2 words)
45 Broken law
46 Former Russian ruler
47 Creative work
48 Mgr.
50 Terminate
54 Caviar
55 First woman
56 Claw
57 Vocal pauses
58 Color
59 What your friend might make you do

DOWN

1 Day in Spain
2 Tool
3 Gnawer
4 Not here
5 Site for friends
6 Feeling for friends
7 Caesar's three
8 Pass, as time
9 Loathe
10 12 Across, for example
11 What friends share
19 Vicar
21 Pursue
22 Hairpin curve
23 With friends, it's okay to act like one

DOWN CONT'D

24 Near-failing grade
25 Says
28 Logger's tool
30 Friendship descriptor
33 Body builder's pride, for short
34 Dove's call
35 Strain, as a system
37 Desired
38 A friend __ positively to you
40 Frighten away
41 Sin
42 Refers to
44 See 40 Across
46 Birch
49 Wall plant
51 __ Baba
52 Sun
53 Girlfriend's name ending, perhaps

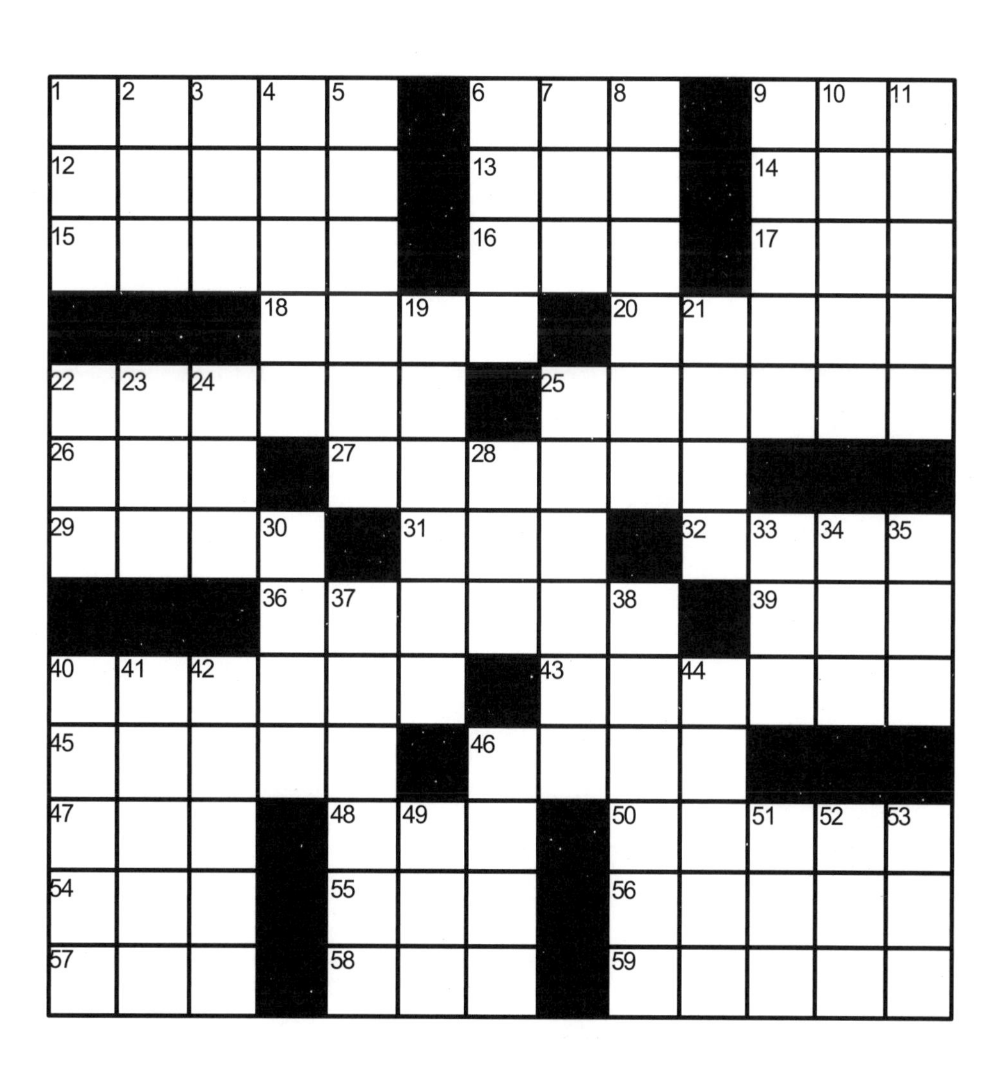

Solutions are in the back.

Good judgement comes from experience,
and a lot of that comes from bad judgement.
Will Rogers

Experience

By our age, we've been around the block, so to speak (perhaps several times). So why aren't folks paying us consultation fees just to hear our sage words of advice? Because they're too busy racing around the block, that's why. So it's left to us to congratulate each other. Pat someone on the back, because they, too, have kicked a few curbs, gotten up, and kept on going. They, too, have turned blind corners and bumped their bean on a light post. Ouch.

We know the neighborhood, and we're here to help each other.

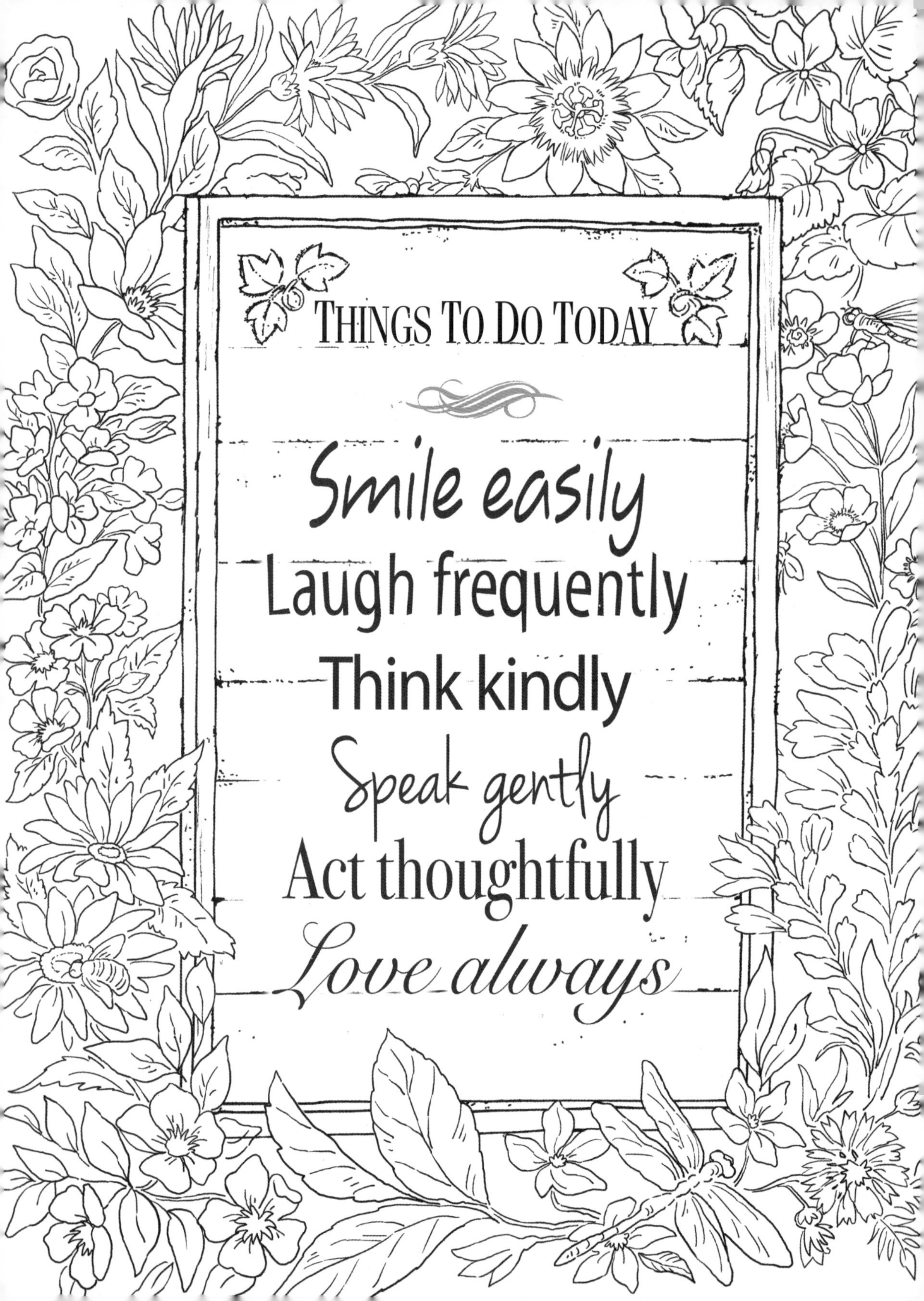
THINGS TO DO TODAY
Smile easily
Laugh frequently
Think kindly
Speak gently
Act thoughtfully
Love always

ASTRONAUT SOLUTION

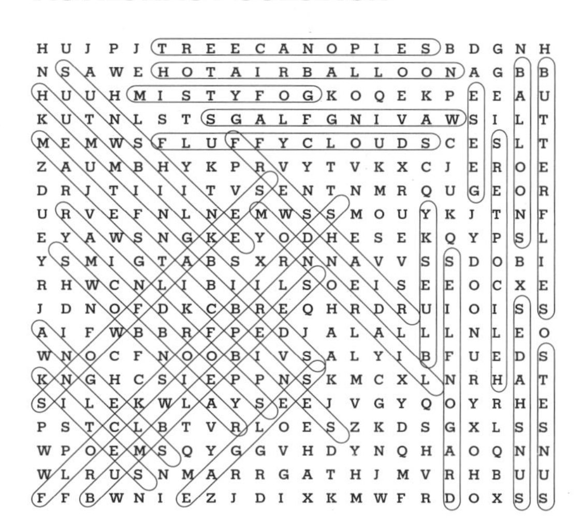

SELFIE SOLUTION

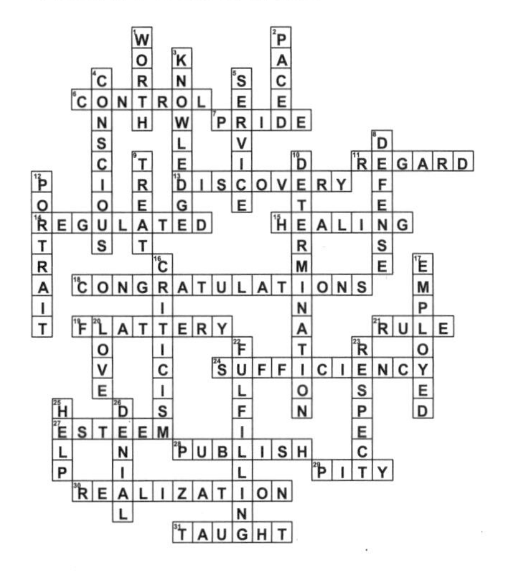

NOAH SOLUTION

1. Two birds added in sky.
2. Plant by tree removed.
3. Dress is longer.
4. Snails are smaller.
5. Noah's belt moved.
6. Butterflies moved.
7. Two windows on ark removed.
8. Noah's wife's hair is longer.
9. Cloud added in sky.

DOLPHIN SOLUTION

GARDEN SOLUTION

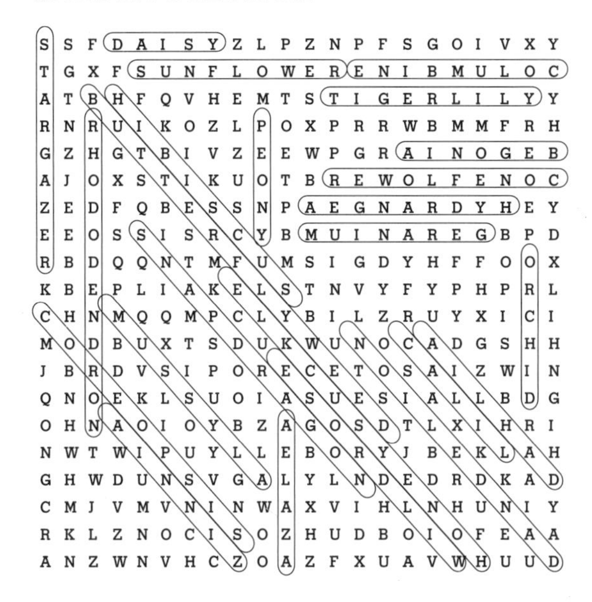

POSITIVE THINKING SOLUTION

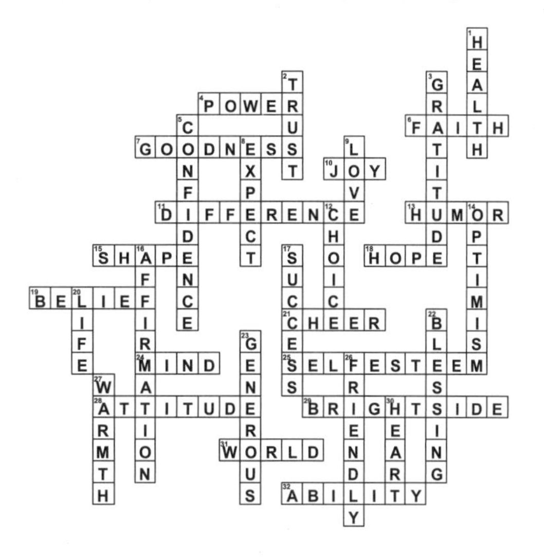

LOAN SOLUTION

1.) Lady's dress is shorter. 2.) Loan Officer sign is different. 3.) Trash can is larger. 4.) Loan officer is holding two pieces of paper. 5.) Pen has moved on desk.

BIRDHOUSE SOLUTION

GRANDMA BAKING SOLUTION

1) Windows are different.
2) Hair bun is added on cooking lady.
3) Apron is added.
4) Drawer changed from 3 to 4.
5) Window on oven is smaller.
6) Calendar months changed.

BRRR! SOLUTION

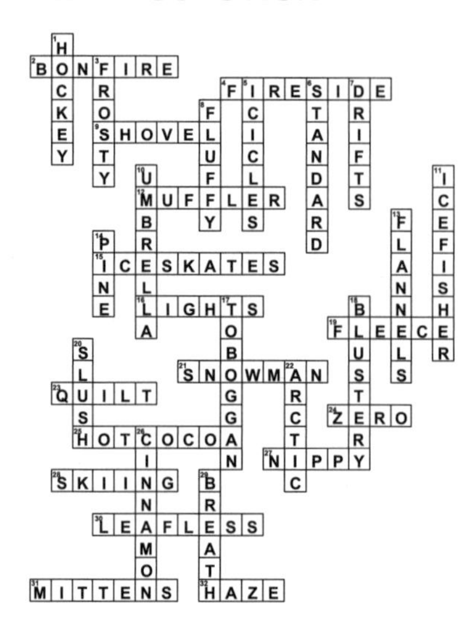

BIRDS SOLUTION

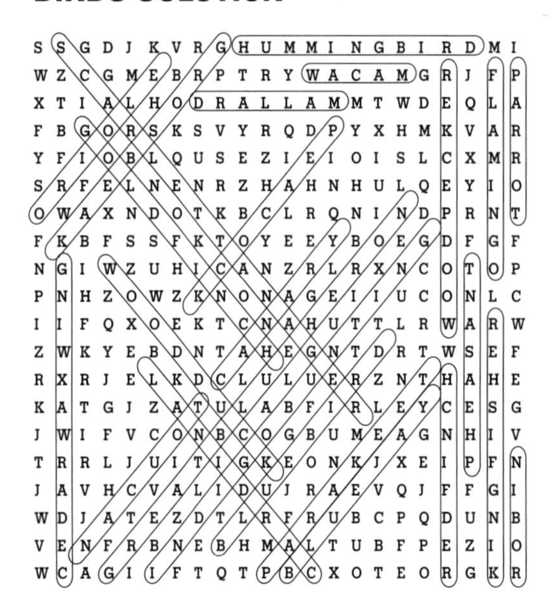

BUCKET LIST SOLUTION

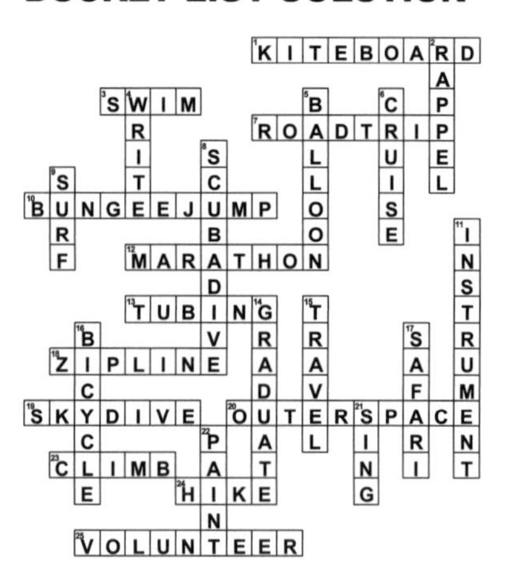

KITTEN BASKET SOLUTION

FEELIN' FINE! SOLUTION

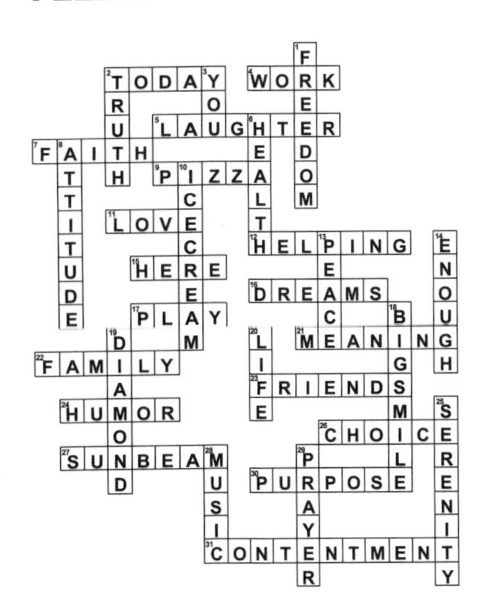

CLASSROOM SOLUTION

1.) Teacher's hair is shorter. 2.) Ruler on desk disappears. 3.) Drawers on desk are different. 4.) Boy in front row is wearing glasses. 5.) Teacher's nose is longer.

WHAT'S NEW SOLUTION

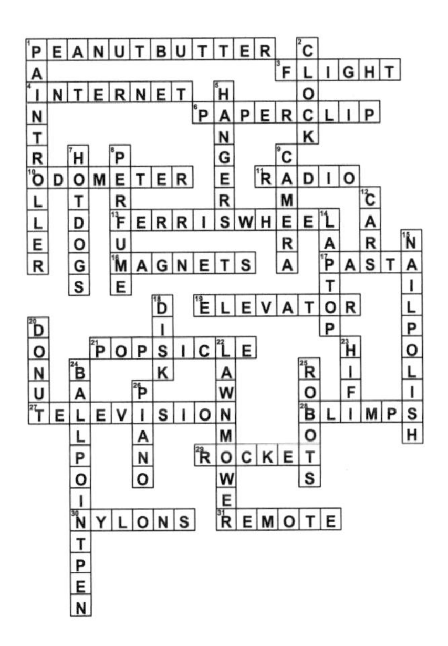

TABLE SOLUTION

1.) Bottom doors are added on cabinet. 2.) Man's shirt sleeve changed. 3.) Baby's hair is different. 4.) Picture on wall has been reversed. 5.) Man's glasses are added.

TOO FUNNY SOLUTION

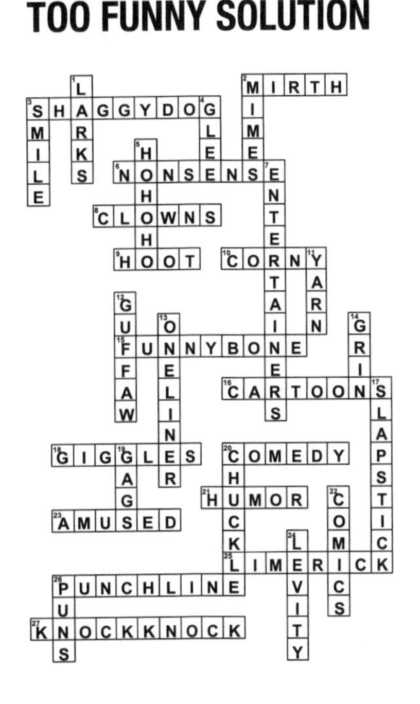

"Three things happen as we age. First, the memory goes. Then...I forget the other two."

CHICKEN SOLUTION

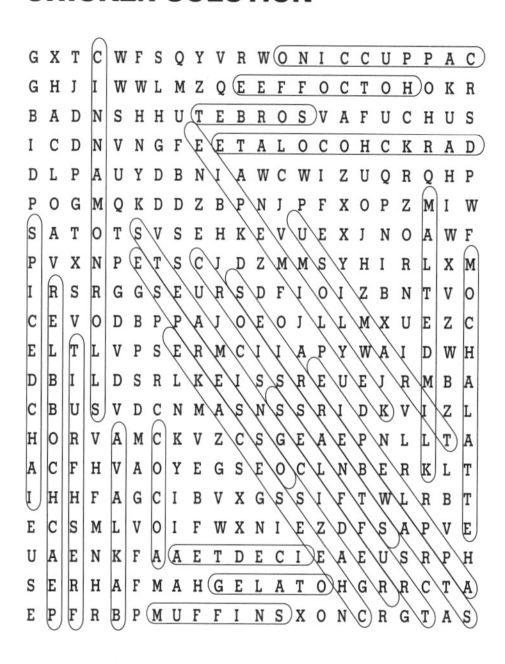

FRIENDS SOLUTION

D	A	R	T	S	■	L	I	E	■	A	S	H
I	D	A	H	O	■	O	I	L	■	B	T	U
A	Z	T	E	C	■	V	I	A	■	H	A	M
■	■	■	R	I	P	E	■	P	H	O	T	O
E	N	D	E	A	R	■	U	S	U	R	E	R
S	U	E	■	L	I	S	T	E	N	■	■	■
S	T	E	W	■	E	A	T	■	T	A	C	T
■	■	■	A	N	S	W	E	R	■	B	O	A
S	E	C	R	E	T	■	R	E	D	S	O	X
C	R	I	M	E	■	T	S	A	R	■	■	■
A	R	T	■	D	I	R	■	C	E	A	S	E
R	O	E	■	E	V	E	■	T	A	L	O	N
E	R	S	■	D	Y	E	■	S	M	I	L	E

Money talks—
but all mine seems to say is
"good-bye!"